The Joy of Beethoven

Selected and edited by Denes Agay.

Ludwig van Beethoven died in March 1827, at the age of 57, and was buried in a Viennese cemetary. According to eyewitness accounts about 20,000 people attended the funeral and since then - for over a century and a half- there has been an unceasing flow of visitors, day in and day out, paying homage at his grave. Such outpouring of reverence, apprecia-tion, and gratitude is unequaled in the annals of music. But then so unique is Beethoven's contribution to music, so powerful and ever-present is the glow of his personality, that he may well be considered a "contemporary" artist even in our 20th century. Certainly, no other composer's works are performed more frequently than his.

Beethoven did not have to struggle for recognition; his genius was perceived almost from the beginning and his name became a household word during his lifetime. The royalty, aristocracy, the intellectual elite of Europe were his friends and pupils and - unlike his outstanding contemporaries, Mozart, Schubert, and others - he had a secure livelihood, free from financial worries, without giving up his fiercely individual life style and ex-alted status as an artist and as a man.

Libraries could be filled with the countless analyses and appreciations of the Beethoven oeuvre. Suffice it to say that, after beginning to write in the classical tradition, he de-veloped his own powerful idiom, different from anything heard before or since in terms of majesty of structure, depth of expression, and projection of drama. His interests took in almost every form of music and he created masterpieces in nearly all media.

While the large works, sonatas, symphonies, concertos and quartets are the true measure of his greatness, he kept busy and delighted in writing in the smaller forms also through-out his creative years. Some of these exquisite miniatures, the bagatelles, sonatinas, albumleaves, songs, and dances - simple in structure and technically not demanding - comprise the contents of this volume, together with easy arrangements of popular themes from his great orchestral works. We hope that this collection will prove to be an ideal first source for partaking of the joys of Beethoven's music.

Denes Agay

© 1983 Yorktown Music Press, Inc.
All Rights Reserved

Order No. YK21251
US ISBN 0.8256.8026.3
UK ISBN 0.7119.0332.8

Exclusive Distributors:
Music Sales Corporation
24 East 22nd Street, New York, NY 10010, USA
Music Sales Limited
78 Newman Street, London W1P 3LA, England
Music Sales Pty. Limited
27 Clarendon Street, Artarmon, Sydney NSW 2064, Australia

Printed in the United States of America by Hamilton Printing Company
2/84

Yorktown Music Press
London/New York/Sydney

CONTENTS

Keyboard Works

Favorite Themes from Concertos and Symphonies
Arranged by Denes Agay

Tyrolean Air
Op. 107, No. 1

Six German Dances

I.

II.

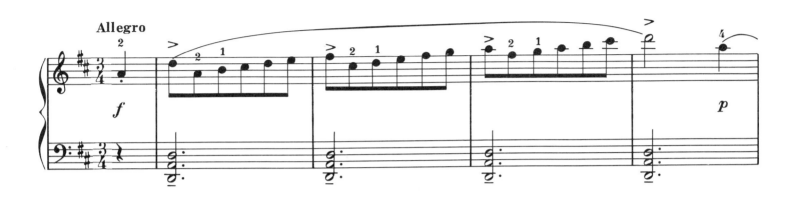

III.

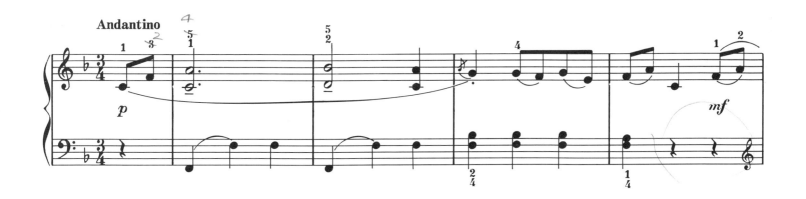

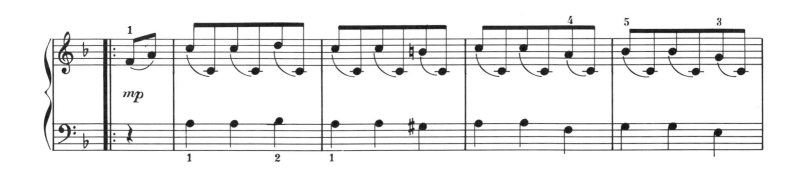

IV.

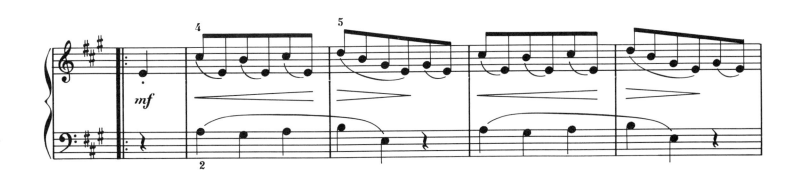

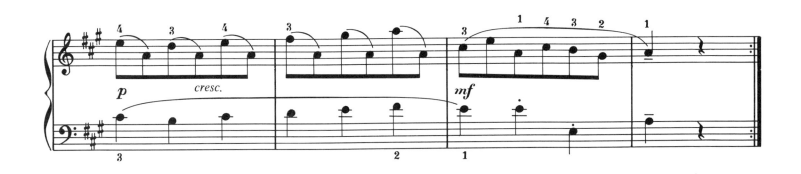

V.

VI.

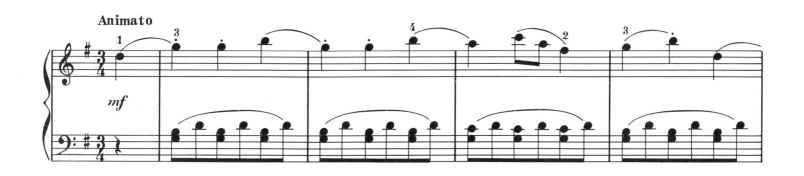

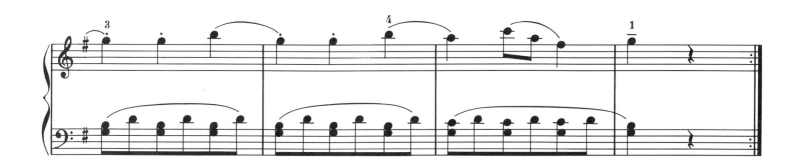

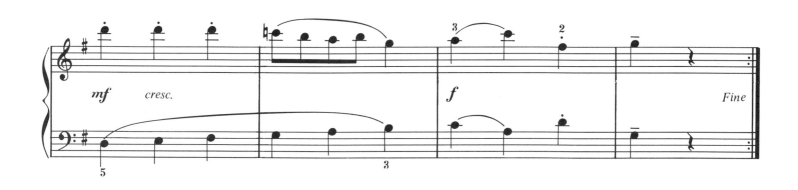

Trio

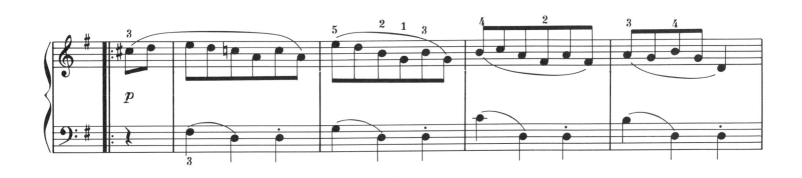

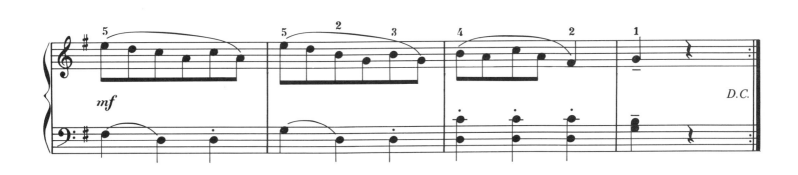

Sonatina
in G

La Marmotte*
Op. 52, No. 7

*Original piano part of the song *La Marmotte*

Walzer
(1824)

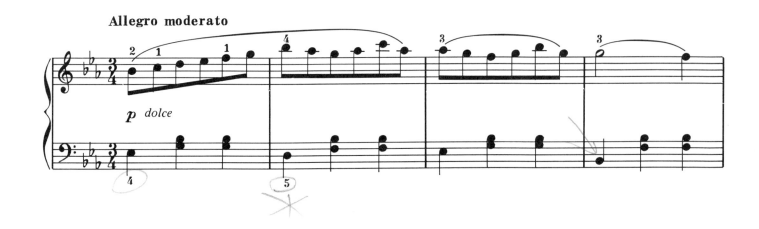

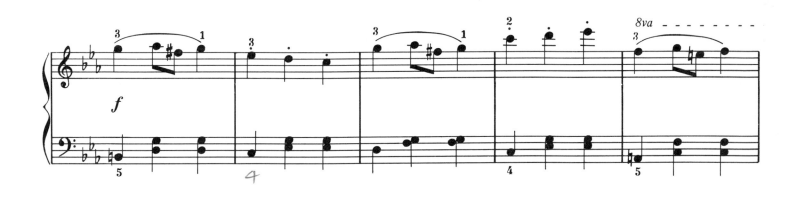

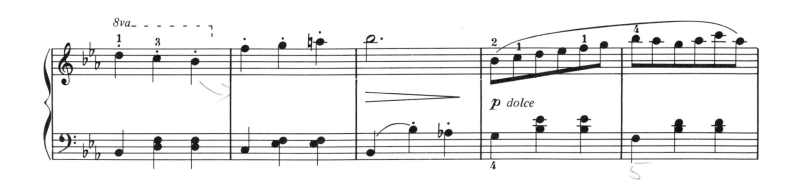

Trio

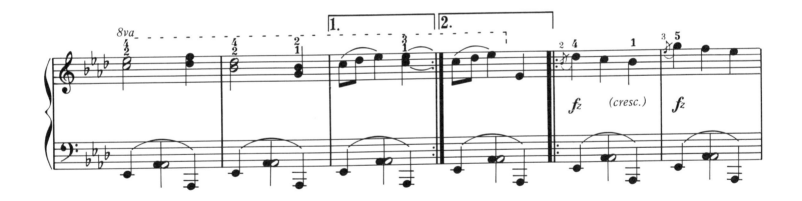

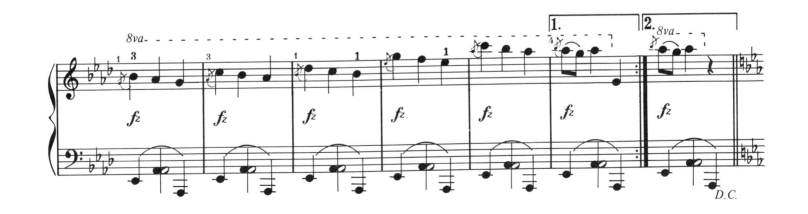

Happy and Sad

Wo O 54

Fine

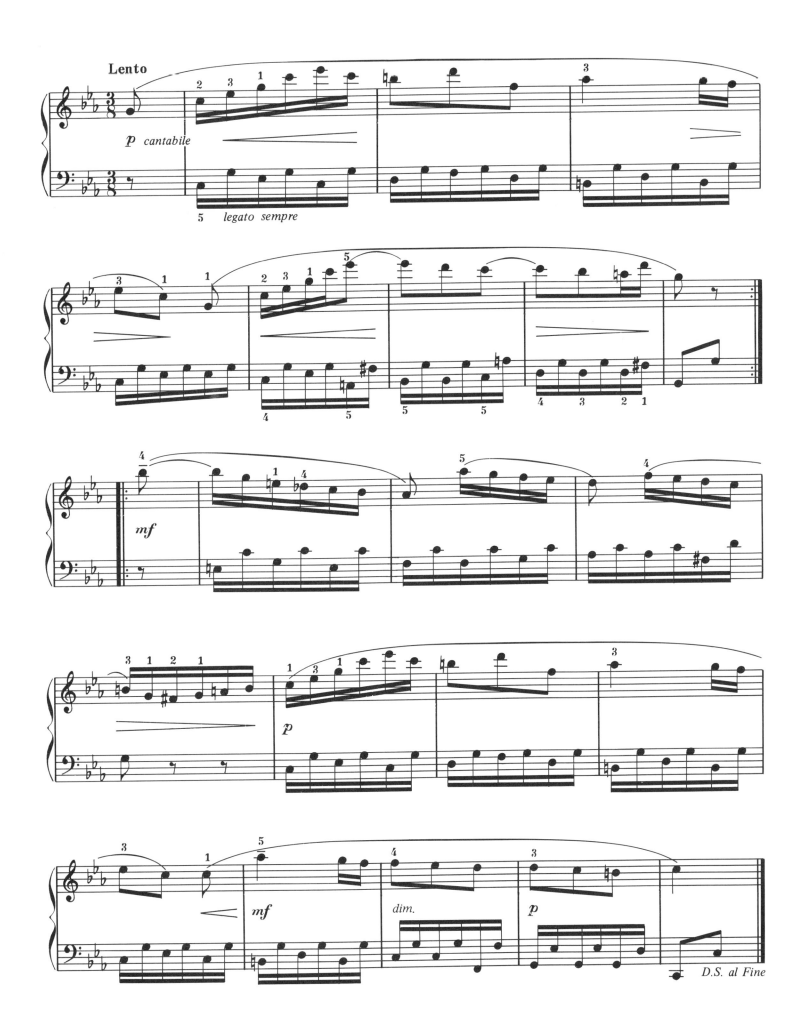

Rondo

WoO 48

Six Ecossaises
(1823)

Für Elise
Klavierstück

Bagatelle
Op. 33, No. 3

Sonata(quasi una Fantasia)

Op. 27, No. 2-First Movement

Adagio sostenuto
Si deve suonare tutto questo pezzo delicatissimamente e senza sordini.

Minuet

Menuetto Da Capo

Bagatelle
Op. 119, No. 4

Andante cantabile

Adagio

from *Easy Sonata in C*

(1791)

*From here completed by Ferdinand Ries

Andante Espressivo

from *Sonata Op. 79* – Second Movement

Bagatelle
Op. 119, No. 2

Andante (con Variazioni)

from *Sonata Op. 14, No. 2* - Second Movement

Variations On A Russian Song

Op. 107, No. 3

55

Piano Piece
(1821)

Sonata
Op. 49, No. 1

Rondo

Allegro

62

Themes from Symphony No. 2

Op. 36 – Second Movement

Theme from Symphony No. 7

Op. 92–Second Movement

Theme from Symphony No. 8

Op. 93-Second Movement

Themes from Piano Concerto No. 3

Op. 37-First Movement

Themes from Piano Concerto No. 1

Op. 15-Third Movement

D.C. al Fine

Theme from Violin Concerto

Op. 61-First Movement

Themes from Symphony No. 5

Op. 67-First Movement (Exposition)